# Spiritual Self-Care

## JOURNAL

urban spirit!

# Now is the time to take responsibility for your own spirituality! Sometimes you just can't make it to the church house.

*The Women of Color Spiritual Self-Care Journal* is a tool designed to help you track, chart and train yourself to reach your goals spiritually!

**There are affirming words** with a corresponding memory verse from the Bible, and a daily self-care checklist with plenty of room to record your reflections, prayers, praises to tell why you are so grateful for the Lord being in your life.

You can doodle, color or draw in this inspirational big book. There is space to lay-out your dreams, plans and goals for the future also.

Select from 2 great covers that look great on any coffee-table or nightstand.

Pick up a copy for yourself and somebody you know that can use this great new tool today!

# How to use this Journal

**The Women of Color Spiritual Self-Care Prayer Journal** is designed to inspire you to take responsibility for your spiritual health! In it you can record important foundational aspects of your life designed to enhance your spiritual awareness and self-care, based on an affirming word, a supporting scripture verse and various reflection and journaling prompts.

Studies have shown that journaling can help you achieve your goals and boost productivity. It is our desire that the Woman of Color Spiritual Self-Care Journal will bring you closer to God and understand how His Word directly impacts your life and everyday actions.

**Affirming Words:** Throughout the journal there are several affirming words. Each affirming word is designed to be a positive reminder that God has planted specific characteristics and/or traits inside you.

**Reflections:** Use the Reflection page to jot down any thoughts you have regarding the affirming word and how this particular trait is demonstrated in your life. During this reflective time, you may discover that this is an area that requires personal growth on your part. Begin to reflect on ways you can begin to display this trait in your life as well as in interactions with others.

**Memory Verse:** Beyond the fact that God commands us to hide His word in our heart (see Deut. 6:4-6), memorizing scripture enables you to fortify your belief in God's word, understand God's eternal promises, and enhances your prayer life. Use the memory verse along with the affirming word as the foundation for the journal prompts that follow each one.

**Praises Going Up:** Gratitude and giving thanks to God for the things He has done is the intent of this space. Establishing a gratitude journal is an excellent way to align what is important to God with what is important to you.

**Count Your Blessings:** This space makes it easy to jot down the many things that God has blessed you with both natural (physical) and spiritual. Keep in mind, blessings are not always tangible. Remember to thank God for things like His mercy and grace, hope and/or deliverance.

**My Prayer Request for Me and for Others:** Prayer is powerful! The Bible promises us that when we pray God hears our hearts (see Jeremiah 29:11; 19:12-13). But just as important as praying to God in spirit, is writing your prayers down. Writing down specific prayer requests for yourself and others means you won't forget what (or who) you prayed for, or what (and who) you prayed about. And, you will always have a quick reference to point to when God answers your prayers.

**My Goals, My Dreams and My Plans:** Scripture reminds us to write the vision and make it plain. Use this space to list out your goals and dreams, and any immediate plans you have to achieve those goals. Always remember to seek God as you plan for your future.

**Self-Care Checklist:** The Self-Care Checklist is a list of simple self-care prompts to ensure that you routinely engage in both physical and spiritual self-care. Use the checklist to keep notes on your progress and what you can do to increase these practices on a daily basis.

**Relaxation Page:** The Relaxation page is an opportunity to express yourself visually. Use the page to color, doodle or draw. Or, color the image provided using the Affirming Word and the Memory Verse to create a visual. Or, use your creativity and draw something personal that makes you happy or brings you joy.

Sketch Art: Melvin Banks, II
Cover and interior designed by Larry P. Taylor

# Spiritual
# Self-Care

## JOURNAL

**urban spirit!**

# Reflections

# I can do all things through **Christ who** strengthens me.

## Philippians 4:13

# Praises Going Up

......................................................................................
......................................................................................
......................................................................................
......................................................................................
......................................................................................
......................................................................................
......................................................................................
......................................................................................

# Count Your Blessings

......................................................................................
......................................................................................
......................................................................................
......................................................................................
......................................................................................
......................................................................................
......................................................................................
......................................................................................
......................................................................................
......................................................................................
......................................................................................

# My Prayer Requests for me

...........................................................

...........................................................

...........................................................

...........................................................

...........................................................

...........................................................

...........................................................

...........................................................

# My Prayer Requests for others

...........................................................

...........................................................

...........................................................

...........................................................

...........................................................

...........................................................

...........................................................

...........................................................

...........................................................

## ◉ My Dreams

........................................................................
........................................................................
........................................................................
........................................................................
........................................................................
........................................................................
........................................................................

## My Goals

........................................................................
........................................................................
........................................................................
........................................................................
........................................................................
........................................................................

## My Plans

........................................................................
........................................................................
........................................................................
........................................................................
........................................................................
........................................................................

# Self Care Checklist:

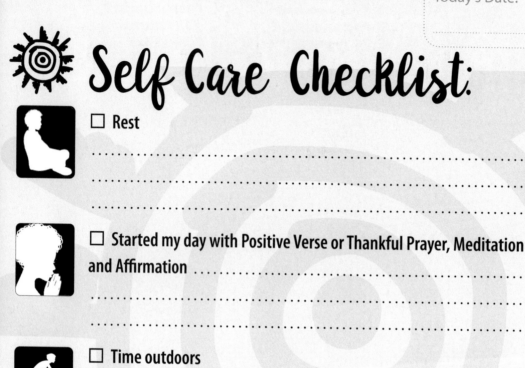

☐ **Rest**

..................................................................................
..................................................................................
..................................................................................

☐ **Started my day with Positive Verse or Thankful Prayer, Meditation and Affirmation** ....................................................................

..................................................................................
..................................................................................

☐ **Time outdoors**

..................................................................................
..................................................................................
..................................................................................

☐ **Drank ample amounts of water**

..................................................................................
..................................................................................
..................................................................................

☐ **Exercised or walked**

..................................................................................
..................................................................................
..................................................................................

☐ **Read a scripture from the Bible, a Christian devotional**

..................................................................................
..................................................................................
..................................................................................

# Self Care Checklist:

☐ **Prayed during the day**

......................................................................................

......................................................................................

......................................................................................

☐ **Connected with a spiritual partner or friend**

......................................................................................

......................................................................................

......................................................................................

......................................................................................

☐ **Prayer before bed**

......................................................................................

......................................................................................

......................................................................................

☐ **Extra prayer for restored or good health**

......................................................................................

......................................................................................

......................................................................................

☐ **More praise to God for goodness given to me!**

......................................................................................

......................................................................................

......................................................................................

☐ **Rest**

......................................................................................

......................................................................................

......................................................................................

# Relaxation
### Color, Doodle, or Draw here

Therefore, if anyone is in Christ, the new creation has come:
The old has gone, the new is here!

**2 Corinthians 5:17**

# Relaxation
### Color, Doodle, or Draw here

# RESILIENT

# Reflections

........................................................................
........................................................................
........................................................................
........................................................................
........................................................................
........................................................................
........................................................................
........................................................................
........................................................................
........................................................................
........................................................................
........................................................................
........................................................................
........................................................................
........................................................................
........................................................................
........................................................................
........................................................................
........................................................................
........................................................................
........................................................................
........................................................................

# We are more
than conquerors
## through Him
that loved us.

**Romans
8:37**

# Praises Going Up

........................................................
........................................................
........................................................
........................................................
........................................................
........................................................
........................................................
........................................................

# Count Your Blessings

........................................................
........................................................
........................................................
........................................................
........................................................
........................................................
........................................................
........................................................
........................................................
........................................................
........................................................

# My Prayer Requests for me

...........................................................................

...........................................................................

...........................................................................

...........................................................................

...........................................................................

...........................................................................

...........................................................................

# My Prayer Requests for others

...........................................................................

...........................................................................

...........................................................................

...........................................................................

...........................................................................

...........................................................................

...........................................................................

...........................................................................

# ☀ My Dreams

...........................................
...........................................
...........................................
...........................................
...........................................
...........................................
...........................................

# My Goals

...........................................
...........................................
...........................................
...........................................
...........................................
...........................................

# My Plans

...........................................
...........................................
...........................................
...........................................
...........................................
...........................................

**21**

# Self Care Checklist:

☐ **Rest**

.................................................................
.................................................................
.................................................................

☐ **Started my day with Positive Verse or Thankful Prayer, Meditation and Affirmation** ...............................................

.................................................................
.................................................................

☐ **Time outdoors**

.................................................................
.................................................................
.................................................................

☐ **Drank ample amounts of water**

.................................................................
.................................................................
.................................................................

☐ **Exercised or walked**

.................................................................
.................................................................
.................................................................

☐ **Read a scripture from the Bible, a Christian devotional**

.................................................................
.................................................................
.................................................................

**22**

# Self Care Checklist:

☐ **Prayed during the day**

.....................................................................................
.....................................................................................
.....................................................................................

☐ **Connected with a spiritual partner or friend**

.....................................................................................
.....................................................................................
.....................................................................................

☐ **Prayer before bed**

.....................................................................................
.....................................................................................
.....................................................................................

☐ **Extra prayer for restored or good health**

.....................................................................................
.....................................................................................
.....................................................................................

☐ **More praise to God for goodness given to me!**

.....................................................................................
.....................................................................................
.....................................................................................

☐ **Rest**

.....................................................................................
.....................................................................................
.....................................................................................

# Relaxation
**Color, Doodle, or Draw here**

Now, my dear, don't worry! I intend to do for you everything you
propose, for everyone in the village knows
that you are a worthy woman.

**R u t h   3 : 1 1**

# Relaxation

**Color, Doodle, or Draw here**

EMPOWERED

# Reflections

# No weapon
formed against me
## shall prosper

**Isaiah 54:17**

# Praises Going Up

........................................................
........................................................
........................................................
........................................................
........................................................
........................................................
........................................................
........................................................
........................................................

# Count Your Blessings

........................................................
........................................................
........................................................
........................................................
........................................................
........................................................
........................................................
........................................................
........................................................
........................................................
........................................................

# My Prayer Requests for me

..................................................................................
..................................................................................
..................................................................................
..................................................................................
..................................................................................
..................................................................................
..................................................................................

# My Prayer Requests for others

..................................................................................
..................................................................................
..................................................................................
..................................................................................
..................................................................................
..................................................................................
..................................................................................
..................................................................................

# ☀ My Dreams

...........................................................
...........................................................
...........................................................
...........................................................
...........................................................
...........................................................
...........................................................

# My Goals

...........................................................
...........................................................
...........................................................
...........................................................
...........................................................
...........................................................

# My Plans

...........................................................
...........................................................
...........................................................
...........................................................
...........................................................
...........................................................

# Self Care Checklist:

☐ Rest

.....................................................................
.....................................................................
.....................................................................

☐ Started my day with Positive Verse or Thankful Prayer, Meditation and Affirmation .................................................
.....................................................................
.....................................................................

☐ Time outdoors

.....................................................................
.....................................................................
.....................................................................

☐ Drank  ample amounts of water

.....................................................................
.....................................................................
.....................................................................

☐ Exercised or walked

.....................................................................
.....................................................................
.....................................................................

☐ Read a scripture from the Bible, a Christian devotional

.....................................................................
.....................................................................
.....................................................................

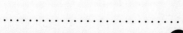

# Self Care Checklist:

☐ **Prayed during the day**

...............................................................................................
...............................................................................................
...............................................................................................

☐ **Connected with a spiritual partner or friend**

...............................................................................................
...............................................................................................
...............................................................................................

☐ **Prayer before bed**

...............................................................................................
...............................................................................................
...............................................................................................

☐ **Extra prayer for restored or good health**

...............................................................................................
...............................................................................................
...............................................................................................

☐ **More praise to God for goodness given to me!**

...............................................................................................
...............................................................................................
...............................................................................................

☐ **Rest**

...............................................................................................
...............................................................................................
...............................................................................................

# Relaxation

Color, Doodle, or Draw here

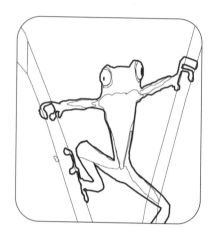

Their land brought forth frogs in abundance,
in the chambers of their kings.

**Psalms 105:30**

# Relaxation
**Color, Doodle, or Draw here**

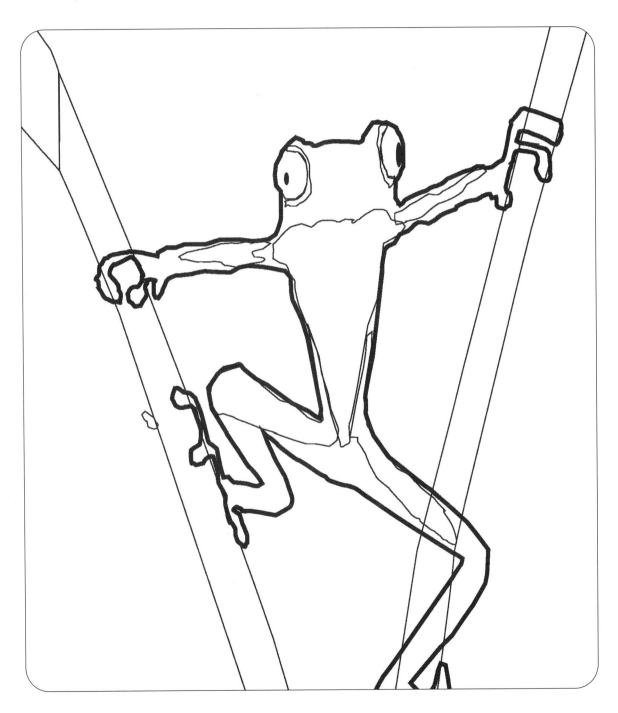

# Reflections

# For I know the plans I have for you, plans to prosper you, not harm you, Plans to give you hope and future.

Jeremiah
29:11

# Praises Going Up

........................................................................
........................................................................
........................................................................
........................................................................
........................................................................
........................................................................
........................................................................
........................................................................
........................................................................

# Count Your Blessings

........................................................................
........................................................................
........................................................................
........................................................................
........................................................................
........................................................................
........................................................................
........................................................................
........................................................................
........................................................................

# My Prayer Requests for me

............................................................
............................................................
............................................................
............................................................
............................................................
............................................................
............................................................
............................................................
............................................................

# My Prayer Requests for others

............................................................
............................................................
............................................................
............................................................
............................................................
............................................................
............................................................
............................................................
............................................................
............................................................

# ◉ My Dreams

..............................................................................
..............................................................................
..............................................................................
..............................................................................
..............................................................................
..............................................................................
..............................................................................

# My Goals

..............................................................................
..............................................................................
..............................................................................
..............................................................................
..............................................................................
..............................................................................

# My Plans

..............................................................................
..............................................................................
..............................................................................
..............................................................................
..............................................................................
..............................................................................

# Self Care Checklist:

☐ Rest

........................................................
........................................................
........................................................

☐ Started my day with Positive Verse or Thankful Prayer, Meditation and Affirmation ...................................
........................................................
........................................................

☐ Time outdoors

........................................................
........................................................
........................................................

☐ Drank ample amounts of water

........................................................
........................................................
........................................................

☐ Exercised or walked

........................................................
........................................................
........................................................

☐ Read a scripture from the Bible, a Christian devotional

........................................................
........................................................
........................................................

# Self Care Checklist:

☐ **Prayed during the day**

..................................................................................
..................................................................................
..................................................................................

☐ **Connected with a spiritual partner or friend**

..................................................................................
..................................................................................
..................................................................................

☐ **Prayer before bed**

..................................................................................
..................................................................................
..................................................................................

☐ **Extra prayer for restored or good health**

..................................................................................
..................................................................................
..................................................................................

☐ **More praise to God for goodness given to me!**

..................................................................................
..................................................................................
..................................................................................

☐ **Rest**

..................................................................................
..................................................................................
..................................................................................

# Relaxation
**Color, Doodle, or Draw here**

According to all that I am going to show you,
as the pattern of the tabernacle and the
pattern of all its furniture, just so you shall construct it.

**E x o d u s   2 5 : 9**

# Relaxation

Color, Doodle, or Draw here

# Reflections

# I will praise
the Lord with my
## whole heart.

# Praises Going Up

## Count Your Blessings

# My Prayer Requests for me

........................................................................
........................................................................
........................................................................
........................................................................
........................................................................
........................................................................
........................................................................
........................................................................
........................................................................

# My Prayer Requests for others

........................................................................
........................................................................
........................................................................
........................................................................
........................................................................
........................................................................
........................................................................
........................................................................
........................................................................

# ☀ My Dreams

····································································

····································································

····································································

····································································

····································································

····································································

····································································

# My Goals

····································································

····································································

····································································

····································································

····································································

····································································

····································································

# My Plans

····································································

····································································

····································································

····································································

····································································

····································································

····································································

# Self Care Checklist:

☐ Rest

...................................................................
...................................................................
...................................................................

☐ Started my day with Positive Verse or Thankful Prayer, Meditation and Affirmation ............................................................

...................................................................
...................................................................

☐ Time outdoors

...................................................................
...................................................................
...................................................................

☐ Drank  ample amounts of water

...................................................................
...................................................................
...................................................................

☐ Exercised or walked

...................................................................
...................................................................
...................................................................

☐ Read a scripture from the Bible, a Christian devotional

...................................................................
...................................................................
...................................................................

# Self Care Checklist:

☐ **Prayed during the day**

.................................................................................
.................................................................................
.................................................................................

☐ **Connected with a spiritual partner or friend**

.................................................................................
.................................................................................
.................................................................................

☐ **Prayer before bed**

.................................................................................
.................................................................................
.................................................................................

☐ **Extra prayer for restored or good health**

.................................................................................
.................................................................................
.................................................................................

☐ **More praise to God for goodness given to me!**

.................................................................................
.................................................................................
.................................................................................

☐ **Rest**

.................................................................................
.................................................................................
.................................................................................

# Relaxation
### Color, Doodle, or Draw here

I am like a pelican of the wilderness:
I am like an owl of the desert, I lie awake,

**Psalm 102:6**

# Relaxation
Color, Doodle, or Draw here

# Reflections

# God will meet all your needs.

## Philippians 4:9

# Praises Going Up

....................................................................................
....................................................................................
....................................................................................
....................................................................................
....................................................................................
....................................................................................
....................................................................................
....................................................................................
....................................................................................

# Count Your Blessings

....................................................................................
....................................................................................
....................................................................................
....................................................................................
....................................................................................
....................................................................................
....................................................................................
....................................................................................
....................................................................................
....................................................................................

# My Prayer Requests for me

........................................................
........................................................
........................................................
........................................................
........................................................
........................................................
........................................................
........................................................
........................................................
........................................................

# My Prayer Requests for others

........................................................
........................................................
........................................................
........................................................
........................................................
........................................................
........................................................
........................................................
........................................................
........................................................
........................................................

# ☀ My Dreams

...............................................................
...............................................................
...............................................................
...............................................................
...............................................................
...............................................................

# My Goals

...............................................................
...............................................................
...............................................................
...............................................................
...............................................................

# My Plans

...............................................................
...............................................................
...............................................................
...............................................................
...............................................................

# Self Care Checklist:

☐ Rest

.................................................................
.................................................................
.................................................................

☐ Started my day with Positive Verse or Thankful Prayer, Meditation and Affirmation .................................................
.................................................................
.................................................................

☐ Time outdoors

.................................................................
.................................................................
.................................................................

☐ Drank ample amounts of water

.................................................................
.................................................................
.................................................................

☐ Exercised or walked

.................................................................
.................................................................
.................................................................

☐ Read a scripture from the Bible, a Christian devotional

.................................................................
.................................................................
.................................................................

# Self Care Checklist:

☐ Prayed during the day

..........................................................................................
..........................................................................................
..........................................................................................

☐ Connected with a spiritual partner or friend

..........................................................................................
..........................................................................................
..........................................................................................

☐ Prayer before bed

..........................................................................................
..........................................................................................
..........................................................................................

☐ Extra prayer for restored or good health

..........................................................................................
..........................................................................................
..........................................................................................

☐ More praise to God for goodness given to me!

..........................................................................................
..........................................................................................
..........................................................................................

☐ Rest

..........................................................................................
..........................................................................................
..........................................................................................

# Relaxation
### Color, Doodle, or Draw here

Can the fig tree, my brethren, bear olive berries?
either a vine, figs? so can no
fountain both yield salt water and fresh.

**JAMES 3:12**

# Relaxation
**Color, Doodle, or Draw here**

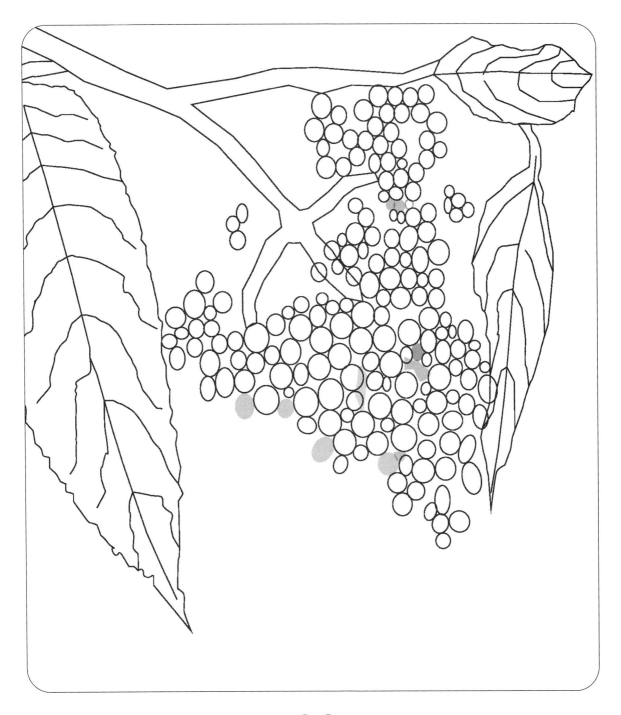

# Reflections

# Fearfully and
## Wonderfully Made

# Psalm 139:14

# Praises Going Up

......................................................................
......................................................................
......................................................................
......................................................................
......................................................................
......................................................................
......................................................................
......................................................................
......................................................................

# Count Your Blessings

......................................................................
......................................................................
......................................................................
......................................................................
......................................................................
......................................................................
......................................................................
......................................................................
......................................................................
......................................................................
......................................................................

# My Prayer Requests for me

...........................................................
...........................................................
...........................................................
...........................................................
...........................................................
...........................................................
...........................................................
...........................................................

# My Prayer Requests for others

...........................................................
...........................................................
...........................................................
...........................................................
...........................................................
...........................................................
...........................................................
...........................................................
...........................................................

# ☀ My Dreams

...........................................................................................
...........................................................................................
...........................................................................................
...........................................................................................
...........................................................................................
...........................................................................................
...........................................................................................

## My Goals

...........................................................................................
...........................................................................................
...........................................................................................
...........................................................................................
...........................................................................................
...........................................................................................

## My Plans

...........................................................................................
...........................................................................................
...........................................................................................
...........................................................................................
...........................................................................................
...........................................................................................

# Self Care Checklist:

☐ **Rest**

......................................................................................

......................................................................................

......................................................................................

☐ **Started my day with Positive Verse or Thankful Prayer, Meditation and Affirmation** ..........................................................

......................................................................................

......................................................................................

☐ **Time outdoors**

......................................................................................

......................................................................................

......................................................................................

☐ **Drank ample amounts of water**

......................................................................................

......................................................................................

......................................................................................

☐ **Exercised or walked**

......................................................................................

......................................................................................

......................................................................................

☐ **Read a scripture from the Bible, a Christian devotional**

......................................................................................

......................................................................................

......................................................................................

# Self Care Checklist:

☐ **Prayed during the day**

..............................................................
..............................................................
..............................................................

☐ **Connected with a spiritual partner or friend**

..............................................................
..............................................................
..............................................................

☐ **Prayer before bed**

..............................................................
..............................................................
..............................................................

☐ **Extra prayer for restored or good health**

..............................................................
..............................................................
..............................................................

☐ **More praise to God for goodness given to me!**

..............................................................
..............................................................
..............................................................

☐ **Rest**

..............................................................
..............................................................
..............................................................

# Relaxation
### Color, Doodle, or Draw here

And he shall be like a tree planted by the rivers of water,
that bringeth forth his fruit in his season; his leaf also shall not wither;
and whatsoever he doeth shall prosper.

**Psalm 1:3**

# Relaxation
### Color, Doodle, or Draw here

Today's Date:

# CONFIDENT

# Reflections

**Trust in the Lord** with all your heart and **lean not on your** own understanding; **in all your ways** acknowledge Him, and **He will make** your paths straight.

**Proverbs 3:5, 6**

# Praises Going Up

........................................................................
........................................................................
........................................................................
........................................................................
........................................................................
........................................................................
........................................................................
........................................................................

# Count Your Blessings

........................................................................
........................................................................
........................................................................
........................................................................
........................................................................
........................................................................
........................................................................
........................................................................
........................................................................

# My Prayer Requests for me

........................................................
........................................................
........................................................
........................................................
........................................................
........................................................
........................................................
........................................................
........................................................
........................................................
........................................................

# My Prayer Requests for others

........................................................
........................................................
........................................................
........................................................
........................................................
........................................................
........................................................
........................................................
........................................................
........................................................
........................................................
........................................................
........................................................

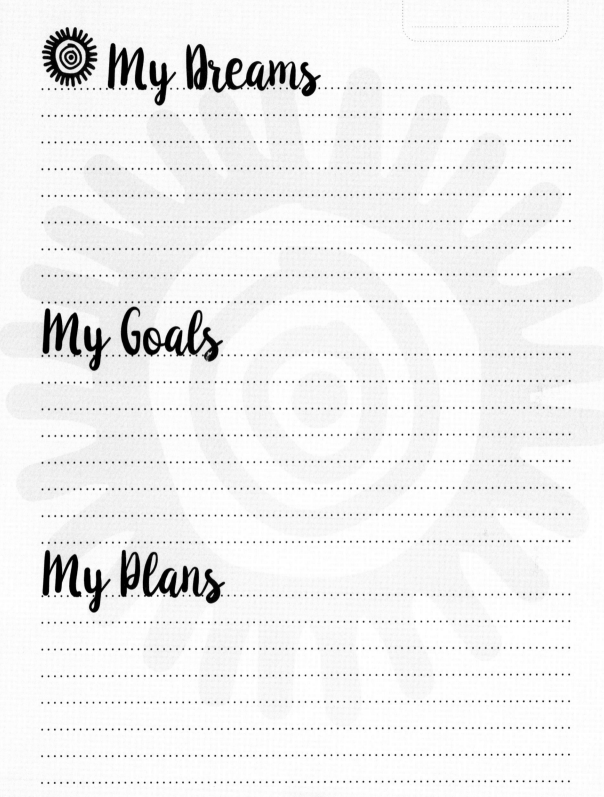

Today's Date:

# ☉ My Dreams

## My Goals

## My Plans

# Self Care Checklist:

☐ **Rest**

....................................................
....................................................
....................................................

 ☐ **Started my day with Positive Verse or Thankful Prayer, Meditation and Affirmation** ....................................................
....................................................
....................................................

 ☐ **Time outdoors**

....................................................
....................................................
....................................................

 ☐ **Drank  ample amounts of water**

....................................................
....................................................
....................................................

 ☐ **Exercised or walked**

....................................................
....................................................
....................................................

   ☐ **Read a scripture from the Bible, a Christian devotional**

....................................................
....................................................
....................................................

# Self Care Checklist:

☐ **Prayed during the day**

........................................................
........................................................
........................................................

☐ **Connected with a spiritual partner or friend**

........................................................
........................................................
........................................................

☐ **Prayer before bed**

........................................................
........................................................
........................................................

☐ **Extra prayer for restored or good health**

........................................................
........................................................
........................................................

☐ **More praise to God for goodness given to me!**

........................................................
........................................................
........................................................

☐ **Rest**

........................................................
........................................................
........................................................

# Relaxation

**Color, Doodle, or Draw here**

He is like a tree planted by flowing streams;
it yields its fruit at the proper time, and its leaves never fall off.
He succeeds in everything he attempts.

**Psalm 1:3**

# Relaxation

### Color, Doodle, or Draw here

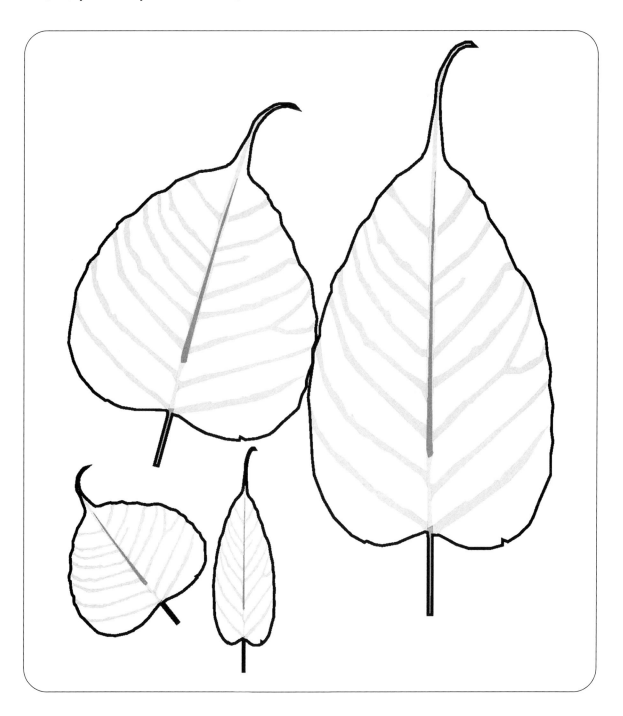

# Reflections

**God not only** loves you very much **but also has put** his hand on you **for something** special.

**1 Thessalonians 1:4**

# Praises Going Up

.......................................................
.......................................................
.......................................................
.......................................................
.......................................................
.......................................................
.......................................................
.......................................................
.......................................................
.......................................................
.......................................................

# Count Your Blessings

.......................................................
.......................................................
.......................................................
.......................................................
.......................................................
.......................................................
.......................................................
.......................................................
.......................................................
.......................................................
.......................................................
.......................................................
.......................................................
.......................................................
.......................................................

# My Prayer Requests for me

······································
······································
······································
······································
······································
······································
······································
······································
······································
······································
······································

# My Prayer Requests for others

······································
······································
······································
······································
······································
······································
······································
······································
······································
······································
······································
······································

Today's Date:
.............

# ⊚ My Dreams

...............................................
...............................................
...............................................
...............................................
...............................................
...............................................
...............................................

# My Goals

...............................................
...............................................
...............................................
...............................................
...............................................
...............................................

# My Plans

...............................................
...............................................
...............................................
...............................................
...............................................
...............................................

# Self Care Checklist:

☐ Rest

....................................................
....................................................
....................................................

☐ Started my day with Positive Verse or Thankful Prayer, Meditation and Affirmation ........................................
....................................................
....................................................

☐ Time outdoors

....................................................
....................................................
....................................................

☐ Drank ample amounts of water

....................................................
....................................................
....................................................

☐ Exercised or walked

....................................................
....................................................
....................................................

☐ Read a scripture from the Bible, a Christian devotional

....................................................
....................................................
....................................................

# Self Care Checklist:

 ☐ **Prayed during the day**

.................................................................................
.................................................................................
.................................................................................

 ☐ **Connected with a spiritual partner or friend**

.................................................................................
.................................................................................
.................................................................................
.................................................................................

 ☐ **Prayer before bed**

.................................................................................
.................................................................................
.................................................................................

 ☐ **Extra prayer for restored or good health**

.................................................................................
.................................................................................
.................................................................................

 ☐ **More praise to God for goodness given to me!**

.................................................................................
.................................................................................
.................................................................................

☐ **Rest**

.................................................................................
.................................................................................
.................................................................................

# Relaxation
**Color, Doodle, or Draw here**

Though it was planted in good soil where water was plentiful
for it to produce leaves and to bear fruit,
it was transplanted, that it might become a splendid vine.

**Ezekiel 17:8**

# Relaxation
**Color, Doodle, or Draw here**

PHENOMENAL

# Reflections

........................................................
........................................................
........................................................
........................................................
........................................................
........................................................
........................................................
........................................................
........................................................
........................................................
........................................................
........................................................
........................................................
........................................................
........................................................
........................................................
........................................................
........................................................
........................................................
........................................................
........................................................
........................................................
........................................................
........................................................
........................................................

# She is clothed
in strength and
**dignity and she**
laughs without
**fear of the**
future.

**Proverbs
31: 25**

# Praises Going Up

..................................................................
..................................................................
..................................................................
..................................................................
..................................................................
..................................................................
..................................................................
..................................................................
..................................................................
..................................................................

# Count Your Blessings

..................................................................
..................................................................
..................................................................
..................................................................
..................................................................
..................................................................
..................................................................
..................................................................
..................................................................
..................................................................
..................................................................
..................................................................
..................................................................

# My Prayer Requests for me

...........................................................
...........................................................
...........................................................
...........................................................
...........................................................
...........................................................
...........................................................
...........................................................
...........................................................
...........................................................

# My Prayer Requests for others

...........................................................
...........................................................
...........................................................
...........................................................
...........................................................
...........................................................
...........................................................
...........................................................
...........................................................
...........................................................

# ☀ My Dreams

........................................................................

........................................................................

........................................................................

........................................................................

........................................................................

........................................................................

# My Goals

........................................................................

........................................................................

........................................................................

........................................................................

........................................................................

# My Plans

........................................................................

........................................................................

........................................................................

........................................................................

........................................................................

........................................................................

**101**

# Self Care Checklist:

☐ **Rest**

.............................................................................
.............................................................................
.............................................................................

☐ **Started my day with Positive Verse or Thankful Prayer, Meditation and Affirmation** .............................................
.............................................................................
.............................................................................

☐ **Time outdoors**

.............................................................................
.............................................................................
.............................................................................

☐ **Drank ample amounts of water**

.............................................................................
.............................................................................
.............................................................................

☐ **Exercised or walked**

.............................................................................
.............................................................................
.............................................................................

☐ **Read a scripture from the Bible, a Christian devotional**

.............................................................................
.............................................................................
.............................................................................

# Self Care Checklist:

☐ **Prayed during the day**

..............................................................
..............................................................
..............................................................

☐ **Connected with a spiritual partner or friend**

..............................................................
..............................................................
..............................................................

☐ **Prayer before bed**

..............................................................
..............................................................
..............................................................

☐ **Extra prayer for restored or good health**

..............................................................
..............................................................
..............................................................

☐ **More praise to God for goodness given to me!**

..............................................................
..............................................................
..............................................................

☐ **Rest**

..............................................................
..............................................................
..............................................................

# Relaxation
### Color, Doodle, or Draw here

He mounted a winged angel and flew;
he glided on the wings of the wind.

**Psalm 18:10**

## Color, Doodle, or Draw here

# COURAGEOUS

# Reflections

# But perfect love

casts out fear.

## 1 John 4: 18

# Praises Going Up

............................................
............................................
............................................
............................................
............................................
............................................
............................................
............................................
............................................

# Count Your Blessings

............................................
............................................
............................................
............................................
............................................
............................................
............................................
............................................
............................................
............................................
............................................
............................................

# My Prayer Requests for me

........................................................
........................................................
........................................................
........................................................
........................................................
........................................................
........................................................
........................................................
........................................................
........................................................
........................................................

# My Prayer Requests for others

........................................................
........................................................
........................................................
........................................................
........................................................
........................................................
........................................................
........................................................
........................................................
........................................................
........................................................
........................................................

# ⊛ My Dreams

.......................................................................
.......................................................................
.......................................................................
.......................................................................
.......................................................................
.......................................................................
.......................................................................

# My Goals

.......................................................................
.......................................................................
.......................................................................
.......................................................................
.......................................................................

# My Plans

.......................................................................
.......................................................................
.......................................................................
.......................................................................
.......................................................................
.......................................................................

**1 1 1**

# Self Care Checklist:

☐ **Rest**

......................................................................
......................................................................
......................................................................

☐ **Started my day with Positive Verse or Thankful Prayer, Meditation and Affirmation** ....................................
......................................................................
......................................................................

☐ **Time outdoors**

......................................................................
......................................................................
......................................................................

☐ **Drank ample amounts of water**

......................................................................
......................................................................
......................................................................

☐ **Exercised or walked**

......................................................................
......................................................................
......................................................................

☐ **Read a scripture from the Bible, a Christian devotional**

......................................................................
......................................................................
......................................................................

**1 1 2**

# Self Care Checklist:

☐ **Prayed during the day**

........................................................................
........................................................................
........................................................................

☐ **Connected with a spiritual partner or friend**

........................................................................
........................................................................
........................................................................

☐ **Prayer before bed**

........................................................................
........................................................................
........................................................................

☐ **Extra prayer for restored or good health**

........................................................................
........................................................................
........................................................................

☐ **More praise to God for goodness given to me!**

........................................................................
........................................................................
........................................................................

☐ **Rest**

........................................................................
........................................................................
........................................................................

# Relaxation
### Color, Doodle, or Draw here

Which hope we have as an anchor of the soul,
both sure and stedfast, and which entereth into
that within the veil

**Hebrews 6:19**

# Relaxation
### Color, Doodle, or Draw here

Today's Date:

# Reflections

# Those who trust
in the Lord will find
# new strength.

## Isaiah 40:31

# Praises Going Up

....................................................

....................................................

....................................................

....................................................

....................................................

....................................................

....................................................

....................................................

# Count Your Blessings

....................................................

....................................................

....................................................

....................................................

....................................................

....................................................

....................................................

....................................................

....................................................

# My Prayer Requests for me

........................................................
........................................................
........................................................
........................................................
........................................................
........................................................
........................................................
........................................................
........................................................
........................................................

# My Prayer Requests for others

........................................................
........................................................
........................................................
........................................................
........................................................
........................................................
........................................................
........................................................
........................................................
........................................................
........................................................

# ☉ My Dreams

.....................................................................................................

.....................................................................................................

.....................................................................................................

.....................................................................................................

.....................................................................................................

.....................................................................................................

.....................................................................................................

# My Goals

.....................................................................................................

.....................................................................................................

.....................................................................................................

.....................................................................................................

.....................................................................................................

.....................................................................................................

# My Plans

.....................................................................................................

.....................................................................................................

.....................................................................................................

.....................................................................................................

.....................................................................................................

.....................................................................................................

.....................................................................................................

# Self Care Checklist:

 ☐ **Rest**

.......................................................
.......................................................
.......................................................

 ☐ **Started my day with Positive Verse or Thankful Prayer, Meditation and Affirmation** ...........................
.......................................................
.......................................................

 ☐ **Time outdoors**

.......................................................
.......................................................
.......................................................

 ☐ **Drank ample amounts of water**

.......................................................
.......................................................
.......................................................

 ☐ **Exercised or walked**

.......................................................
.......................................................
.......................................................

 ☐ **Read a scripture from the Bible, a Christian devotional**

.......................................................
.......................................................
.......................................................

# Self Care Checklist:

 ☐ **Prayed during the day**

...........................................................................
...........................................................................
...........................................................................

 ☐ **Connected with a spiritual partner or friend**

...........................................................................
...........................................................................
...........................................................................

 ☐ **Prayer before bed**

...........................................................................
...........................................................................
...........................................................................

 ☐ **Extra prayer for restored or good health**

...........................................................................
...........................................................................
...........................................................................

 ☐ **More praise to God for goodness given to me!**

...........................................................................
...........................................................................
...........................................................................

 ☐ **Rest**

...........................................................................
...........................................................................
...........................................................................

**1 2 3**

# Relaxation
### Color, Doodle, or Draw here

And let her take off the dress in which she was made prisoner
and go on living in your house and weeping for her father and mother
for a full month: and after that you may go in to her and be
her husband and she will be your wife.

**Deuteronomy 21:13**

# Relaxation
**Color, Doodle, or Draw here**

# Reflections

# O Lord my God,
I cried out to You
# and You healed me.

## Psalm 30: 2

# Praises Going Up

......................................................................
......................................................................
......................................................................
......................................................................
......................................................................
......................................................................
......................................................................
......................................................................

# Count Your Blessings

......................................................................
......................................................................
......................................................................
......................................................................
......................................................................
......................................................................
......................................................................
......................................................................
......................................................................

# ◉ My Prayer Requests for me

........................................................
........................................................
........................................................
........................................................
........................................................
........................................................
........................................................
........................................................
........................................................

# My Prayer Requests for others

........................................................
........................................................
........................................................
........................................................
........................................................
........................................................
........................................................
........................................................
........................................................
........................................................

# ✺ My Dreams

..................................................................................
..................................................................................
..................................................................................
..................................................................................
..................................................................................
..................................................................................

# My Goals

..................................................................................
..................................................................................
..................................................................................
..................................................................................
..................................................................................

# My Plans

..................................................................................
..................................................................................
..................................................................................
..................................................................................
..................................................................................

# Self Care Checklist:

☐ Rest

..............................................................
..............................................................
..............................................................

☐ Started my day with Positive Verse or Thankful Prayer, Meditation and Affirmation ..............................................
..............................................................
..............................................................

☐ Time outdoors

..............................................................
..............................................................
..............................................................

☐ Drank  ample amounts of water

..............................................................
..............................................................
..............................................................

☐ Exercised or walked

..............................................................
..............................................................
..............................................................

☐ Read a scripture from the Bible, a Christian devotional

..............................................................
..............................................................
..............................................................

# Self Care Checklist:

☐ **Prayed during the day**

......................................................................................
......................................................................................
......................................................................................

☐ **Connected with a spiritual partner or friend**

......................................................................................
......................................................................................
......................................................................................
......................................................................................

☐ **Prayer before bed**

......................................................................................
......................................................................................
......................................................................................

☐ **Extra prayer for restored or good health**

......................................................................................
......................................................................................
......................................................................................

☐ **More praise to God for goodness given to me!**

......................................................................................
......................................................................................
......................................................................................

☐ **Rest**

......................................................................................
......................................................................................
......................................................................................

# Relaxation

**Color, Doodle, or Draw here**

Banish emotional stress from your mind. and put away pain from your body; for youth and the prime of life are fleeting.

**Ecclesiastes 11:10**

# Relaxation
## Color, Doodle, or Draw here

Today's Date:

# Reflections

# And we know that
all things work together
## for good to those
who are the called
## according to his
purpose.

**Romans 8:28**

# Praises Going Up

...................................................................
...................................................................
...................................................................
...................................................................
...................................................................
...................................................................
...................................................................
...................................................................

# Count Your Blessings

...................................................................
...................................................................
...................................................................
...................................................................
...................................................................
...................................................................
...................................................................
...................................................................
...................................................................

# My Prayer Requests for me

..........................................................................

..........................................................................

..........................................................................

..........................................................................

..........................................................................

..........................................................................

..........................................................................

..........................................................................

# My Prayer Requests for others

..........................................................................

..........................................................................

..........................................................................

..........................................................................

..........................................................................

..........................................................................

..........................................................................

..........................................................................

..........................................................................

# ☀ My Dreams

..............................................................................................
..............................................................................................
..............................................................................................
..............................................................................................
..............................................................................................
..............................................................................................
..............................................................................................
..............................................................................................

# My Goals

..............................................................................................
..............................................................................................
..............................................................................................
..............................................................................................
..............................................................................................
..............................................................................................

# My Plans

..............................................................................................
..............................................................................................
..............................................................................................
..............................................................................................
..............................................................................................
..............................................................................................

# Self Care Checklist:

☐ Rest

.................................................................
.................................................................
.................................................................

☐ Started my day with Positive Verse or Thankful Prayer, Meditation and Affirmation .................................................
.................................................................
.................................................................

☐ Time outdoors

.................................................................
.................................................................
.................................................................

☐ Drank  ample amounts of water

.................................................................
.................................................................
.................................................................

☐ Exercised or walked

.................................................................
.................................................................
.................................................................

☐ Read a scripture from the Bible, a Christian devotional

.................................................................
.................................................................
.................................................................

① ④ ②

 # Self Care Checklist:

☐ **Prayed during the day**

. . . . . . . . . . . . . . . . . . . . . . . . . . . . . . . . . . . . . . . . . . . . . . . . . . . . . . . . . . . . . . . . . . . . . . . . . .
. . . . . . . . . . . . . . . . . . . . . . . . . . . . . . . . . . . . . . . . . . . . . . . . . . . . . . . . . . . . . . . . . . . . . . . . . .
. . . . . . . . . . . . . . . . . . . . . . . . . . . . . . . . . . . . . . . . . . . . . . . . . . . . . . . . . . . . . . . . . . . . . . . . . .

☐ **Connected with a spiritual partner or friend**

. . . . . . . . . . . . . . . . . . . . . . . . . . . . . . . . . . . . . . . . . . . . . . . . . . . . . . . . . . . . . . . . . . . . . . . . . .
. . . . . . . . . . . . . . . . . . . . . . . . . . . . . . . . . . . . . . . . . . . . . . . . . . . . . . . . . . . . . . . . . . . . . . . . . .
. . . . . . . . . . . . . . . . . . . . . . . . . . . . . . . . . . . . . . . . . . . . . . . . . . . . . . . . . . . . . . . . . . . . . . . . . .

☐ **Prayer before bed**

. . . . . . . . . . . . . . . . . . . . . . . . . . . . . . . . . . . . . . . . . . . . . . . . . . . . . . . . . . . . . . . . . . . . . . . . . .
. . . . . . . . . . . . . . . . . . . . . . . . . . . . . . . . . . . . . . . . . . . . . . . . . . . . . . . . . . . . . . . . . . . . . . . . . .
. . . . . . . . . . . . . . . . . . . . . . . . . . . . . . . . . . . . . . . . . . . . . . . . . . . . . . . . . . . . . . . . . . . . . . . . . .

☐ **Extra prayer for restored or good health**

. . . . . . . . . . . . . . . . . . . . . . . . . . . . . . . . . . . . . . . . . . . . . . . . . . . . . . . . . . . . . . . . . . . . . . . . . .
. . . . . . . . . . . . . . . . . . . . . . . . . . . . . . . . . . . . . . . . . . . . . . . . . . . . . . . . . . . . . . . . . . . . . . . . . .
. . . . . . . . . . . . . . . . . . . . . . . . . . . . . . . . . . . . . . . . . . . . . . . . . . . . . . . . . . . . . . . . . . . . . . . . . .

☐ **More praise to God for goodness given to me!**

. . . . . . . . . . . . . . . . . . . . . . . . . . . . . . . . . . . . . . . . . . . . . . . . . . . . . . . . . . . . . . . . . . . . . . . . . .
. . . . . . . . . . . . . . . . . . . . . . . . . . . . . . . . . . . . . . . . . . . . . . . . . . . . . . . . . . . . . . . . . . . . . . . . . .
. . . . . . . . . . . . . . . . . . . . . . . . . . . . . . . . . . . . . . . . . . . . . . . . . . . . . . . . . . . . . . . . . . . . . . . . . .

☐ **Rest**

. . . . . . . . . . . . . . . . . . . . . . . . . . . . . . . . . . . . . . . . . . . . . . . . . . . . . . . . . . . . . . . . . . . . . . . . . .
. . . . . . . . . . . . . . . . . . . . . . . . . . . . . . . . . . . . . . . . . . . . . . . . . . . . . . . . . . . . . . . . . . . . . . . . . .
. . . . . . . . . . . . . . . . . . . . . . . . . . . . . . . . . . . . . . . . . . . . . . . . . . . . . . . . . . . . . . . . . . . . . . . . . .

# Relaxation
## Color, Doodle, or Draw here

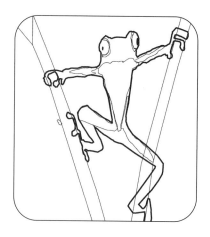

And Aaron stretcheth out his hand against the waters of Egypt,
and the frog cometh up, and covereth the land of Egypt;

**Exodus 8:6**

# Relaxation

**Color, Doodle, or Draw here**

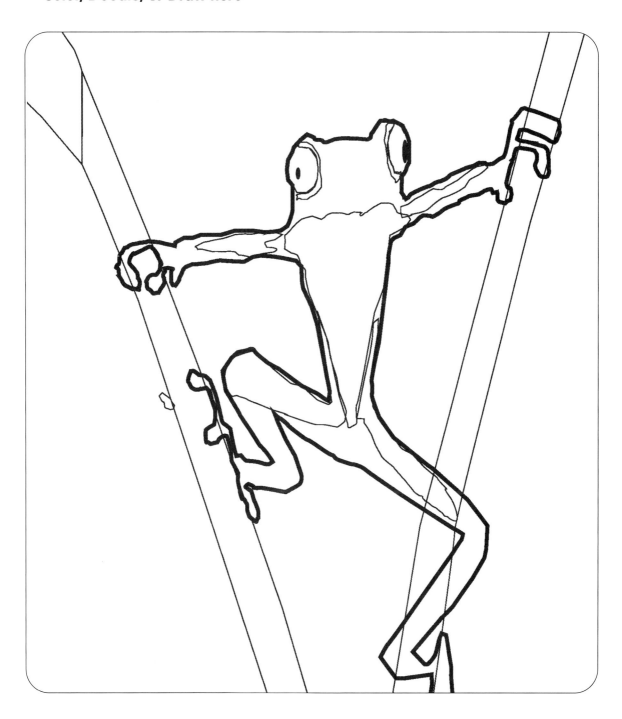

1 4 5

# Reflections

# God is my strength
and my power;
**and he maketh**
my way perfect.

**2 Samuel
22:33**

# Praises Going Up

................................................................
................................................................
................................................................
................................................................
................................................................
................................................................
................................................................
................................................................
................................................................

# Count Your Blessings

................................................................
................................................................
................................................................
................................................................
................................................................
................................................................
................................................................
................................................................
................................................................
................................................................
................................................................
................................................................

# My Prayer Requests for me

...................................................................
...................................................................
...................................................................
...................................................................
...................................................................
...................................................................
...................................................................
...................................................................

# My Prayer Requests for others

...................................................................
...................................................................
...................................................................
...................................................................
...................................................................
...................................................................
...................................................................
...................................................................
...................................................................

# ◉ My Dreams

........................................................
........................................................
........................................................
........................................................
........................................................
........................................................

# My Goals

........................................................
........................................................
........................................................
........................................................
........................................................
........................................................

# My Plans

........................................................
........................................................
........................................................
........................................................
........................................................
........................................................

# Self Care Checklist:

 ☐ Rest

......................................................
......................................................
......................................................

 ☐ Started my day with Positive Verse or Thankful Prayer, Meditation and Affirmation

......................................................
......................................................
......................................................

 ☐ Time outdoors

......................................................
......................................................
......................................................

 ☐ Drank ample amounts of water

......................................................
......................................................
......................................................

 ☐ Exercised or walked

......................................................
......................................................
......................................................

 ☐ Read a scripture from the Bible, a Christian devotional

......................................................
......................................................
......................................................

**1 5 2**

# Self Care Checklist:

☐ **Prayed during the day**

........................................................................................
........................................................................................
........................................................................................

☐ **Connected with a spiritual partner or friend**

........................................................................................
........................................................................................
........................................................................................

☐ **Prayer before bed**

........................................................................................
........................................................................................
........................................................................................

☐ **Extra prayer for restored or good health**

........................................................................................
........................................................................................
........................................................................................

☐ **More praise to God for goodness given to me!**

........................................................................................
........................................................................................

☐ **Rest**

........................................................................................
........................................................................................
........................................................................................

# Relaxation
### Color, Doodle, or Draw here

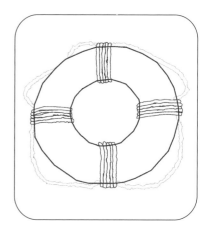

for this we labour and suffer reproach, because we hope i
n a living God, who is preserver of all men,
specially of those that believe.

**1 Timothy 4:10**

# Relaxation
### Color, Doodle, or Draw here

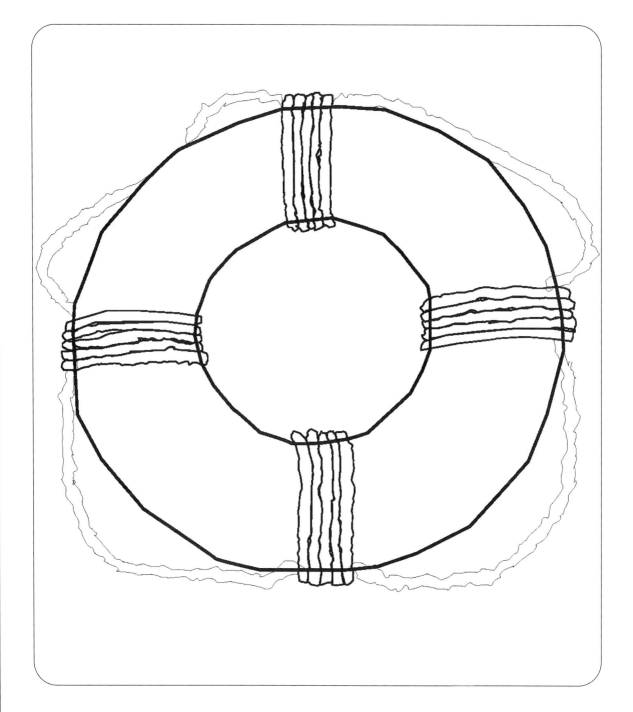

# Reflections

# Ask, and

it shall be given you;

## seek, and ye shall find;

knock,

## and it shall be

opened unto you.

## Mathew 7:7

# Praises Going Up

........................................................
........................................................
........................................................
........................................................
........................................................
........................................................
........................................................
........................................................
........................................................
........................................................

# Count Your Blessings

........................................................
........................................................
........................................................
........................................................
........................................................
........................................................
........................................................
........................................................
........................................................
........................................................
........................................................

# My Prayer Requests for me

........................................................
........................................................
........................................................
........................................................
........................................................
........................................................
........................................................
........................................................
........................................................
........................................................
........................................................
........................................................

# My Prayer Requests for others

........................................................
........................................................
........................................................
........................................................
........................................................
........................................................
........................................................
........................................................
........................................................
........................................................
........................................................
........................................................
........................................................

# ◉ My Dreams

...........................................................................
...........................................................................
...........................................................................
...........................................................................
...........................................................................
...........................................................................

# My Goals

...........................................................................
...........................................................................
...........................................................................
...........................................................................
...........................................................................

# My Plans

...........................................................................
...........................................................................
...........................................................................
...........................................................................
...........................................................................

# Self Care Checklist:

 ☐ Rest

·······································································
·······································································
·······································································

 ☐ Started my day with Positive Verse or Thankful Prayer, Meditation and Affirmation ·······································

·······································································
·······································································

 ☐ Time outdoors

·······································································
·······································································
·······································································

 ☐ Drank ample amounts of water

·······································································
·······································································
·······································································

 ☐ Exercised or walked

·······································································
·······································································
·······································································

 ☐ Read a scripture from the Bible, a Christian devotional

·······································································
·······································································
·······································································

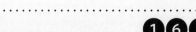

# Self Care Checklist:

☐ **Prayed during the day**

.................................................................................
.................................................................................
.................................................................................

☐ **Connected with a spiritual partner or friend**

.................................................................................
.................................................................................
.................................................................................

☐ **Prayer before bed**

.................................................................................
.................................................................................
.................................................................................

☐ **Extra prayer for restored or good health**

.................................................................................
.................................................................................
.................................................................................

☐ **More praise to God for goodness given to me!**

.................................................................................
.................................................................................
.................................................................................

☐ **Rest**

.................................................................................
.................................................................................
.................................................................................

# Relaxation
**Color, Doodle, or Draw here**

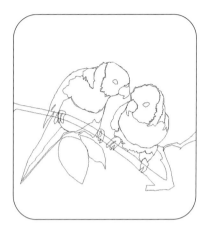

Two of every sort of bird and cattle and of every sort of living thing
which goes on the earth will you take with you
to keep them from destruction.

**Genesis 6:20**

# Relaxation
**Color, Doodle, or Draw here**

Today's Date:

# Reflections

# Trust in God with
all your heart.

## Proverbs 3:5

# Praises Going Up

........................................................

........................................................

........................................................

........................................................

........................................................

........................................................

........................................................

........................................................

........................................................

........................................................

# Count Your Blessings

........................................................

........................................................

........................................................

........................................................

........................................................

........................................................

........................................................

........................................................

........................................................

........................................................

........................................................

# My Prayer Requests for me

........................................................
........................................................
........................................................
........................................................
........................................................
........................................................
........................................................
........................................................
........................................................
........................................................
........................................................
........................................................
........................................................

# My Prayer Requests for others

........................................................
........................................................
........................................................
........................................................
........................................................
........................................................
........................................................
........................................................
........................................................
........................................................
........................................................
........................................................
........................................................

# ☼ My Dreams

...................................................................................
...................................................................................
...................................................................................
...................................................................................
...................................................................................
...................................................................................
...................................................................................

# My Goals

...................................................................................
...................................................................................
...................................................................................
...................................................................................
...................................................................................

# My Plans

...................................................................................
...................................................................................
...................................................................................
...................................................................................
...................................................................................

# Self Care Checklist:

☐ Rest

.................................................................................

.................................................................................

.................................................................................

☐ Started my day with Positive Verse or Thankful Prayer, Meditation and Affirmation .................................................................

.................................................................................

.................................................................................

☐ Time outdoors

.................................................................................

.................................................................................

.................................................................................

☐ Drank ample amounts of water

.................................................................................

.................................................................................

.................................................................................

☐ Exercised or walked

.................................................................................

.................................................................................

.................................................................................

☐ Read a scripture from the Bible, a Christian devotional

.................................................................................

.................................................................................

.................................................................................

# Self Care Checklist:

 ☐ **Prayed during the day**

..................................................................................
..................................................................................
..................................................................................

 ☐ **Connected with a spiritual partner or friend**

..................................................................................
..................................................................................
..................................................................................

 ☐ **Prayer before bed**

..................................................................................
..................................................................................
..................................................................................

 ☐ **Extra prayer for restored or good health**

..................................................................................
..................................................................................
..................................................................................

 ☐ **More praise to God for goodness given to me!**

..................................................................................
..................................................................................
..................................................................................

 ☐ **Rest**

..................................................................................
..................................................................................
..................................................................................

**1 7 3**

# Relaxation
### Color, Doodle, or Draw here

Now it happened that on one of the days both he
and his disciples got into a boat, and he said to them,
"Let us cross over to the other side of the lake." And they set sail,

**Luke 8:22**

# Relaxation
## Color, Doodle, or Draw here

# Reflections

**The Lord bless thee** and keep thee: **The Lord make His** face shine upon thee, **and be gracious** unto thee.

**Numbers
6: 24,25**

# Praises Going Up

..................................................................
..................................................................
..................................................................
..................................................................
..................................................................
..................................................................
..................................................................
..................................................................
..................................................................
..................................................................

# Count Your Blessings

..................................................................
..................................................................
..................................................................
..................................................................
..................................................................
..................................................................
..................................................................
..................................................................
..................................................................
..................................................................
..................................................................

# My Prayer Requests for me

......................................................
......................................................
......................................................
......................................................
......................................................
......................................................
......................................................
......................................................
......................................................

# My Prayer Requests for others

......................................................
......................................................
......................................................
......................................................
......................................................
......................................................
......................................................
......................................................
......................................................
......................................................
......................................................

# ◎ My Dreams

..........................................................................
..........................................................................
..........................................................................
..........................................................................
..........................................................................
..........................................................................
..........................................................................

# My Goals

..........................................................................
..........................................................................
..........................................................................
..........................................................................
..........................................................................
..........................................................................

# My Plans

..........................................................................
..........................................................................
..........................................................................
..........................................................................
..........................................................................
..........................................................................
..........................................................................

Today's Date:

# Self Care Checklist:

☐ Rest

..............................................................
..............................................................
..............................................................

☐ Started my day with Positive Verse or Thankful Prayer, Meditation and Affirmation ...........................................

..............................................................
..............................................................

☐ Time outdoors

..............................................................
..............................................................
..............................................................

☐ Drank ample amounts of water

..............................................................
..............................................................
..............................................................

☐ Exercised or walked

..............................................................
..............................................................
..............................................................

☐ Read a scripture from the Bible, a Christian devotional

..............................................................
..............................................................
..............................................................

visit our website: www.urbanspirit.biz

Today's Date:

 # Self Care Checklist:

☐ **Prayed during the day**

..............................................................................
..............................................................................
..............................................................................

 ☐ **Connected with a spiritual partner or friend**

..............................................................................
..............................................................................
..............................................................................

 ☐ **Prayer before bed**

..............................................................................
..............................................................................
..............................................................................

 ☐ **Extra prayer for restored or good health**

..............................................................................
..............................................................................
..............................................................................

 ☐ **More praise to God for goodness given to me!**

..............................................................................
..............................................................................
..............................................................................

 ☐ **Rest**

..............................................................................
..............................................................................
..............................................................................

**1** **8** **3**

# Relaxation
### Color, Doodle, or Draw here

So they set sail. While they were sailing he fell asleep.
And there fell on the lake a squall of wind, so that the boat began to fill,
and they to be in deadly peril.

**Luke 8:23**

# Relaxation

Color, Doodle, or Draw here

# Reflections

# This is the day

that the Lord has made.

## Lets rejoice and

be glad in it.

**Psalm 118:24**

# Praises Going Up

........................................................................
........................................................................
........................................................................
........................................................................
........................................................................
........................................................................
........................................................................
........................................................................
........................................................................
........................................................................

# Count Your Blessings

........................................................................
........................................................................
........................................................................
........................................................................
........................................................................
........................................................................
........................................................................
........................................................................
........................................................................
........................................................................
........................................................................
........................................................................
........................................................................

# My Prayer Requests for me

........................................................................
........................................................................
........................................................................
........................................................................
........................................................................
........................................................................
........................................................................
........................................................................
........................................................................

# My Prayer Requests for others

........................................................................
........................................................................
........................................................................
........................................................................
........................................................................
........................................................................
........................................................................
........................................................................
........................................................................
........................................................................

# ☀ My Dreams

........................................................................
........................................................................
........................................................................
........................................................................
........................................................................
........................................................................
........................................................................

# My Goals

........................................................................
........................................................................
........................................................................
........................................................................
........................................................................

# My Plans

........................................................................
........................................................................
........................................................................
........................................................................
........................................................................
........................................................................

# Self Care Checklist:

 ☐ Rest

.................................................................
.................................................................
.................................................................

 ☐ Started my day with Positive Verse or Thankful Prayer, Meditation and Affirmation ...................................................

.................................................................
.................................................................

 ☐ Time outdoors

.................................................................
.................................................................
.................................................................

 ☐ Drank ample amounts of water

.................................................................
.................................................................
.................................................................

 ☐ Exercised or walked

.................................................................
.................................................................
.................................................................

 ☐ Read a scripture from the Bible, a Christian devotional

.................................................................
.................................................................
.................................................................

# Self Care Checklist:

☐ **Prayed during the day**

.................................................................
.................................................................
.................................................................

☐ **Connected with a spiritual partner or friend**

.................................................................
.................................................................
.................................................................

☐ **Prayer before bed**

.................................................................
.................................................................
.................................................................

☐ **Extra prayer for restored or good health**

.................................................................
.................................................................
.................................................................

☐ **More praise to God for goodness given to me!**

.................................................................
.................................................................
.................................................................

☐ **Rest**

.................................................................
.................................................................
.................................................................

# Relaxation

**Color, Doodle, or Draw here**

And the earth brought forth grass, and herb yielding seed
after his kind, and the tree yielding fruit, whose seed was in itself,
after his kind: and God saw that it was good.

**Genesis 1:12**

# Relaxation
## Color, Doodle, or Draw here

# Reflections

# I carried you
on eagles' wings,

**Exodus
19:4**

## Praises Going Up

........................................................

........................................................

........................................................

........................................................

........................................................

........................................................

........................................................

........................................................

........................................................

........................................................

## Count Your Blessings

........................................................

........................................................

........................................................

........................................................

........................................................

........................................................

........................................................

........................................................

........................................................

........................................................

........................................................

# My Prayer Requests for me

........................................................
........................................................
........................................................
........................................................
........................................................
........................................................
........................................................
........................................................
........................................................

# My Prayer Requests for others

........................................................
........................................................
........................................................
........................................................
........................................................
........................................................
........................................................
........................................................
........................................................
........................................................

# ◎ My Dreams

.................................................................................
.................................................................................
.................................................................................
.................................................................................
.................................................................................
.................................................................................

# My Goals

.................................................................................
.................................................................................
.................................................................................
.................................................................................
.................................................................................
.................................................................................

# My Plans

.................................................................................
.................................................................................
.................................................................................
.................................................................................
.................................................................................
.................................................................................

Today's Date:

# Self Care Checklist:

☐ Rest

.......................................................................
.......................................................................
.......................................................................

☐ Started my day with Positive Verse or Thankful Prayer, Meditation and Affirmation .............................................

.......................................................................
.......................................................................

☐ Time outdoors

.......................................................................
.......................................................................
.......................................................................

☐ Drank ample amounts of water

.......................................................................
.......................................................................
.......................................................................

☐ Exercised or walked

.......................................................................
.......................................................................
.......................................................................

☐ Read a scripture from the Bible, a Christian devotional

.......................................................................
.......................................................................
.......................................................................

# Self Care Checklist:

 ☐ **Prayed during the day**

..................................................................
..................................................................
..................................................................

 ☐ **Connected with a spiritual partner or friend**

..................................................................
..................................................................
..................................................................

 ☐ **Prayer before bed**

..................................................................
..................................................................
..................................................................

 ☐ **Extra prayer for restored or good health**

..................................................................
..................................................................
..................................................................

 ☐ **More praise to God for goodness given to me!**

..................................................................
..................................................................
..................................................................

 ☐ **Rest**

..................................................................
..................................................................
..................................................................

# Relaxation
### Color, Doodle, or Draw here

Then God said,..; and to every beast of the earth and to every bird of the sky and to every thing that moves on the earth which has life, I have given every green plant for food"; and it was so.

**Genesis 1:29,30**

# Relaxation

**Color, Doodle, or Draw here**

Today's Date:

# Reflections

# Do not worry

about tomorrow.

## Mathew
## 6:39

# Praises Going Up

.................................................................................
.................................................................................
.................................................................................
.................................................................................
.................................................................................
.................................................................................
.................................................................................
.................................................................................
.................................................................................

# Count Your Blessings

.................................................................................
.................................................................................
.................................................................................
.................................................................................
.................................................................................
.................................................................................
.................................................................................
.................................................................................
.................................................................................
.................................................................................
.................................................................................

# My Prayer Requests for me

# My Prayer Requests for others

# ☀ My Dreams

..............................................................................
..............................................................................
..............................................................................
..............................................................................
..............................................................................
..............................................................................
..............................................................................

# My Goals

..............................................................................
..............................................................................
..............................................................................
..............................................................................
..............................................................................
..............................................................................

# My Plans

..............................................................................
..............................................................................
..............................................................................
..............................................................................
..............................................................................
..............................................................................

# Self Care Checklist:

☐ Rest

.........................................................................
.........................................................................
.........................................................................

☐ Started my day with Positive Verse or Thankful Prayer, Meditation and Affirmation .........................................

.........................................................................
.........................................................................

☐ Time outdoors

.........................................................................
.........................................................................
.........................................................................

☐ Drank  ample amounts of water

.........................................................................
.........................................................................
.........................................................................

☐ Exercised or walked

.........................................................................
.........................................................................
.........................................................................

☐ Read a scripture from the Bible, a Christian devotional

.........................................................................
.........................................................................
.........................................................................

**2 1 2**

# Self Care Checklist:

☐ **Prayed during the day**

.........................................................................................
.........................................................................................
.........................................................................................

☐ **Connected with a spiritual partner or friend**

.........................................................................................
.........................................................................................
.........................................................................................

☐ **Prayer before bed**

.........................................................................................
.........................................................................................
.........................................................................................

☐ **Extra prayer for restored or good health**

.........................................................................................
.........................................................................................
.........................................................................................

☐ **More praise to God for goodness given to me!**

.........................................................................................
.........................................................................................
.........................................................................................

☐ **Rest**

.........................................................................................
.........................................................................................
.........................................................................................

# Relaxation
**Color, Doodle, or Draw here**

But if a woman have long hair,
it is a glory to her: for her hair is given her for a covering

**1 Corinthians 11:15**

# Relaxation

**Color, Doodle, or Draw here**

Today's Date:

# Reflections

# By the grace of God,

I am what I am.

## I Corinthians
## 15:10 NIV

# Praises Going Up

........................................................................
........................................................................
........................................................................
........................................................................
........................................................................
........................................................................
........................................................................
........................................................................

# Count Your Blessings

........................................................................
........................................................................
........................................................................
........................................................................
........................................................................
........................................................................
........................................................................
........................................................................
........................................................................

# My Prayer Requests for me

......................................................
......................................................
......................................................
......................................................
......................................................
......................................................
......................................................
......................................................
......................................................
......................................................
......................................................

# My Prayer Requests for others

......................................................
......................................................
......................................................
......................................................
......................................................
......................................................
......................................................
......................................................
......................................................
......................................................
......................................................

# ◉ My Dreams

......................................................................
......................................................................
......................................................................
......................................................................
......................................................................
......................................................................
......................................................................

# My Goals

......................................................................
......................................................................
......................................................................
......................................................................
......................................................................
......................................................................
......................................................................

# My Plans

......................................................................
......................................................................
......................................................................
......................................................................
......................................................................
......................................................................
......................................................................

# *Self Care Checklist:*

☐ **Rest**

........................................................
........................................................
........................................................

 ☐ **Started my day with Positive Verse or Thankful Prayer, Meditation and Affirmation** ...........

........................................................
........................................................

 ☐ **Time outdoors**

........................................................
........................................................
........................................................

 ☐ **Drank ample amounts of water**

........................................................
........................................................
........................................................

 ☐ **Exercised or walked**

........................................................
........................................................
........................................................

 ☐ **Read a scripture from the Bible, a Christian devotional**

........................................................
........................................................
........................................................

**2 2 2**

# Self Care Checklist:

☐ **Prayed during the day**

.......................................................................................
.......................................................................................
.......................................................................................

☐ **Connected with a spiritual partner or friend**

.......................................................................................
.......................................................................................
.......................................................................................

☐ **Prayer before bed**

.......................................................................................
.......................................................................................
.......................................................................................

☐ **Extra prayer for restored or good health**

.......................................................................................
.......................................................................................
.......................................................................................

☐ **More praise to God for goodness given to me!**

.......................................................................................
.......................................................................................
.......................................................................................

☐ **Rest**

.......................................................................................
.......................................................................................
.......................................................................................

# Relaxation
### Color, Doodle, or Draw here

The Lord reigns! The nations tremble.
He sits enthroned above the winged angels; the earth shakes.

**Psalms 99:1**

# Relaxation
## Color, Doodle, or Draw here

Today's Date:

# Reflections

# God not only
loves you very much
## but also has put
His hand on you
## for something special.

**I Thessalonians
1:4**

# Praises Going Up

............................................................

............................................................

............................................................

............................................................

............................................................

............................................................

............................................................

............................................................

............................................................

# Count Your Blessings

............................................................

............................................................

............................................................

............................................................

............................................................

............................................................

............................................................

............................................................

............................................................

............................................................

............................................................

# My Prayer Requests for me

.................................................................................
.................................................................................
.................................................................................
.................................................................................
.................................................................................
.................................................................................
.................................................................................
.................................................................................
.................................................................................

# My Prayer Requests for others

.................................................................................
.................................................................................
.................................................................................
.................................................................................
.................................................................................
.................................................................................
.................................................................................
.................................................................................
.................................................................................
.................................................................................
.................................................................................

# My Dreams

......................................................................................

........................................................................................

........................................................................................

........................................................................................

........................................................................................

........................................................................................

# My Goals

........................................................................................

........................................................................................

........................................................................................

........................................................................................

........................................................................................

# My Plans

........................................................................................

........................................................................................

........................................................................................

........................................................................................

........................................................................................

# Self Care Checklist:

☐ Rest

...........................................................
...........................................................
...........................................................

☐ Started my day with Positive Verse or Thankful Prayer, Meditation and Affirmation ..........................................
...........................................................
...........................................................

☐ Time outdoors

...........................................................
...........................................................
...........................................................

☐ Drank  ample amounts of water

...........................................................
...........................................................
...........................................................

☐ Exercised or walked

...........................................................
...........................................................
...........................................................

☐ Read a scripture from the Bible, a Christian devotional

...........................................................
...........................................................
...........................................................

# Self Care Checklist:

☐ **Prayed during the day**

..............................................................................
..............................................................................
..............................................................................

☐ **Connected with a spiritual partner or friend**

..............................................................................
..............................................................................
..............................................................................

☐ **Prayer before bed**

..............................................................................
..............................................................................
..............................................................................

☐ **Extra prayer for restored or good health**

..............................................................................
..............................................................................
..............................................................................

☐ **More praise to God for goodness given to me!**

..............................................................................
..............................................................................
..............................................................................

☐ **Rest**

..............................................................................
..............................................................................
..............................................................................

# Relaxation
### Color, Doodle, or Draw here

Therefore, if anyone is in Christ, the new creation has come:
The old has gone, the new is here!

**2 Corinthians 5:17**

# Relaxation
### Color, Doodle, or Draw here

CREATIVE

# Reflections

# Now to Him who
is able to do
## exceedingly
abundantly above all
## that we ask or think,
according to the power
## that works in us,
to Him be glory.

**Ephesians
3:20-21 NKJV**

# Praises Going Up

........................................................
........................................................
........................................................
........................................................
........................................................
........................................................
........................................................
........................................................
........................................................
........................................................

# Count Your Blessings

........................................................
........................................................
........................................................
........................................................
........................................................
........................................................
........................................................
........................................................
........................................................
........................................................
........................................................

# My Prayer Requests for me

....................................................

....................................................

....................................................

....................................................

....................................................

....................................................

....................................................

....................................................

....................................................

# My Prayer Requests for others

....................................................

....................................................

....................................................

....................................................

....................................................

....................................................

....................................................

....................................................

....................................................

....................................................

....................................................

....................................................

# My Dreams

....................................................................................
....................................................................................
....................................................................................
....................................................................................
....................................................................................
....................................................................................
....................................................................................
....................................................................................

# My Goals

....................................................................................
....................................................................................
....................................................................................
....................................................................................
....................................................................................

# My Plans

....................................................................................
....................................................................................
....................................................................................
....................................................................................
....................................................................................
....................................................................................
....................................................................................

**2 4 1**

# Self Care Checklist:

☐ Rest

...................................................................
...................................................................
...................................................................

☐ Started my day with Positive Verse or Thankful Prayer, Meditation
and Affirmation ...................................................
...................................................................
...................................................................

☐ Time outdoors

...................................................................
...................................................................
...................................................................

☐ Drank ample amounts of water

...................................................................
...................................................................
...................................................................

☐ Exercised or walked

...................................................................
...................................................................

☐ Read a scripture from the Bible, a Christian devotional

...................................................................
...................................................................
...................................................................

# Self Care Checklist:

☐ **Prayed during the day**

.......................................................................
.......................................................................
.......................................................................

☐ **Connected with a spiritual partner or friend**

.......................................................................
.......................................................................
.......................................................................

☐ **Prayer before bed**

.......................................................................
.......................................................................
.......................................................................

☐ **Extra prayer for restored or good health**

.......................................................................
.......................................................................
.......................................................................

☐ **More praise to God for goodness given to me!**

.......................................................................
.......................................................................
.......................................................................

 ☐ **Rest**

.......................................................................
.......................................................................
.......................................................................

# Relaxation
### Color, Doodle, or Draw here

Now, my dear, don't worry! I intend to do for you everything you
propose, for everyone in the village knows
that you are a worthy woman.

**Ruth 3:11**

# Relaxation

**Color, Doodle, or Draw here**

# Reflections

**Taste and see that** the Lord is good. **Oh, the joys of those** who trust in Him!

**Psalm 34:8**

# Praises Going Up

........................................................................
........................................................................
........................................................................
........................................................................
........................................................................
........................................................................
........................................................................
........................................................................
........................................................................

# Count Your Blessings

........................................................................
........................................................................
........................................................................
........................................................................
........................................................................
........................................................................
........................................................................
........................................................................
........................................................................
........................................................................
........................................................................
........................................................................
........................................................................

# My Prayer Requests for me

····································
····································
····································
····································
····································
····································
····································
····································
····································
····································
····································

# My Prayer Requests for others

····································
····································
····································
····································
····································
····································
····································
····································
····································
····································
····································
····································

# ◎ My Dreams

..................................................................................
..................................................................................
..................................................................................
..................................................................................
..................................................................................
..................................................................................
..................................................................................

# My Goals

..................................................................................
..................................................................................
..................................................................................
..................................................................................
..................................................................................
..................................................................................

# My Plans

..................................................................................
..................................................................................
..................................................................................
..................................................................................
..................................................................................
..................................................................................

# Self Care Checklist:

 ☐ Rest

......................................................................
......................................................................
......................................................................

 ☐ Started my day with Positive Verse or Thankful Prayer, Meditation and Affirmation ..................................................

......................................................................
......................................................................

 ☐ Time outdoors

......................................................................
......................................................................
......................................................................

 ☐ Drank ample amounts of water

......................................................................
......................................................................
......................................................................

 ☐ Exercised or walked

......................................................................
......................................................................
......................................................................

 ☐ Read a scripture from the Bible, a Christian devotional

......................................................................
......................................................................
......................................................................

**252**

# Self Care Checklist:

☐ **Prayed during the day**

.......................................................................................
.......................................................................................
.......................................................................................

☐ **Connected with a spiritual partner or friend**

.......................................................................................
.......................................................................................
.......................................................................................

☐ **Prayer before bed**

.......................................................................................
.......................................................................................
.......................................................................................

☐ **Extra prayer for restored or good health**

.......................................................................................
.......................................................................................
.......................................................................................

☐ **More praise to God for goodness given to me!**

.......................................................................................
.......................................................................................
.......................................................................................

☐ **Rest**

.......................................................................................
.......................................................................................
.......................................................................................

# Relaxation
### Color, Doodle, or Draw here

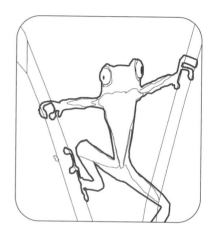

Their land brought forth frogs in abundance,
in the chambers of their kings.

**Psalms 105:30**

# Relaxation
**Color, Doodle, or Draw here**

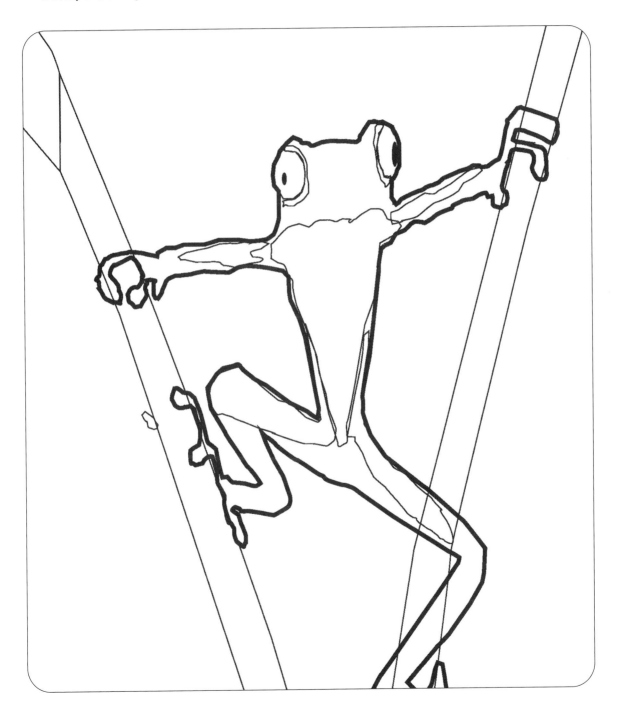

# Reflections

.......................................................................
.......................................................................
.......................................................................
.......................................................................
.......................................................................
.......................................................................
.......................................................................
.......................................................................
.......................................................................
.......................................................................
.......................................................................
.......................................................................
.......................................................................
.......................................................................
.......................................................................
.......................................................................
.......................................................................
.......................................................................
.......................................................................
.......................................................................
.......................................................................
.......................................................................
.......................................................................
.......................................................................
.......................................................................
.......................................................................

**Whatever is true,** whatever is noble, **whatever is right,** whatever is pure, **whatever is lovely...** think about such **things.**

**Philippians 4:8**

# Praises Going Up

........................................................

........................................................

........................................................

........................................................

........................................................

........................................................

........................................................

........................................................

# Count Your Blessings

........................................................

........................................................

........................................................

........................................................

........................................................

........................................................

........................................................

........................................................

........................................................

........................................................

........................................................

# My Prayer Requests for me

........................................................
........................................................
........................................................
........................................................
........................................................
........................................................
........................................................
........................................................
........................................................
........................................................

# My Prayer Requests for others

........................................................
........................................................
........................................................
........................................................
........................................................
........................................................
........................................................
........................................................
........................................................
........................................................

# ☉ My Dreams

........................................................................

........................................................................

........................................................................

........................................................................

........................................................................

........................................................................

# My Goals

........................................................................

........................................................................

........................................................................

........................................................................

........................................................................

........................................................................

# My Plans

........................................................................

........................................................................

........................................................................

........................................................................

........................................................................

........................................................................

# Self Care Checklist:

☐ Rest

..................................................................................
..................................................................................
..................................................................................

☐ Started my day with Positive Verse or Thankful Prayer, Meditation and Affirmation ........................................................

..................................................................................
..................................................................................

☐ Time outdoors

..................................................................................
..................................................................................
..................................................................................

☐ Drank ample amounts of water

..................................................................................
..................................................................................
..................................................................................

☐ Exercised or walked

..................................................................................
..................................................................................
..................................................................................

☐ Read a scripture from the Bible, a Christian devotional

..................................................................................
..................................................................................
..................................................................................

# Self Care Checklist:

☐ **Prayed during the day**

......................................................................
......................................................................
......................................................................

 ☐ **Connected with a spiritual partner or friend**

......................................................................
......................................................................
......................................................................

 ☐ **Prayer before bed**

......................................................................
......................................................................
......................................................................

 ☐ **Extra prayer for restored or good health**

......................................................................
......................................................................
......................................................................

 ☐ **More praise to God for goodness given to me!**

......................................................................
......................................................................
......................................................................

 ☐ **Rest**

......................................................................
......................................................................
......................................................................

# Relaxation
**Color, Doodle, or Draw here**

According to all that I am going to show you,
as the pattern of the tabernacle and the
pattern of all its furniture, just so you shall construct it.

**Exodus 25:9**

# Relaxation

## Color, Doodle, or Draw here

# HONORABLE

# Reflections

# Be joyful in hope, patient in affliction, faithful in prayer.

## Romans 12:12 NIV

# Praises Going Up

.......................................................

.......................................................

.......................................................

.......................................................

.......................................................

.......................................................

.......................................................

.......................................................

# Count Your Blessings

.......................................................

.......................................................

.......................................................

.......................................................

.......................................................

.......................................................

.......................................................

.......................................................

.......................................................

.......................................................

.......................................................

# My Prayer Requests for me

........................................................................................................
........................................................................................................
........................................................................................................
........................................................................................................
........................................................................................................
........................................................................................................
........................................................................................................
........................................................................................................
........................................................................................................
........................................................................................................
........................................................................................................

# My Prayer Requests for others

........................................................................................................
........................................................................................................
........................................................................................................
........................................................................................................
........................................................................................................
........................................................................................................
........................................................................................................
........................................................................................................
........................................................................................................
........................................................................................................

# ☀ My Dreams

.................................................................................................................
.................................................................................................................
.................................................................................................................
.................................................................................................................
.................................................................................................................
.................................................................................................................
.................................................................................................................

# My Goals

.................................................................................................................
.................................................................................................................
.................................................................................................................
.................................................................................................................
.................................................................................................................

# My Plans

.................................................................................................................
.................................................................................................................
.................................................................................................................
.................................................................................................................
.................................................................................................................
.................................................................................................................

# Self Care Checklist:

☐ Rest

.......................................................................
.......................................................................
.......................................................................

☐ Started my day with Positive Verse or Thankful Prayer, Meditation and Affirmation ...............................................

.......................................................................
.......................................................................
.......................................................................

☐ Time outdoors

.......................................................................
.......................................................................
.......................................................................

☐ Drank ample amounts of water

.......................................................................
.......................................................................
.......................................................................

☐ Exercised or walked

.......................................................................
.......................................................................
.......................................................................

☐ Read a scripture from the Bible, a Christian devotional

.......................................................................
.......................................................................
.......................................................................

# Self Care Checklist:

☐ **Prayed during the day**

.................................................................
.................................................................
.................................................................

☐ **Connected with a spiritual partner or friend**

.................................................................
.................................................................
.................................................................

☐ **Prayer before bed**

.................................................................
.................................................................
.................................................................

☐ **Extra prayer for restored or good health**

.................................................................
.................................................................
.................................................................

☐ **More praise to God for goodness given to me!**

.................................................................
.................................................................
.................................................................

☐ **Rest**

.................................................................
.................................................................
.................................................................

# Relaxation
**Color, Doodle, or Draw here**

I am like a pelican of the wilderness:
I am like an owl of the desert, I lie awake,

**Psalm 102:6**

# Relaxation
**Color, Doodle, or Draw here**

visit our website: www.urbanspirit.biz

# COMING SOON!

KING JAMES VERSION

WOMEN of COLOR
STUDY BIBLE

# WOMEN COLOR
## DAILY DEVOTIONAL

Spring
EDITION

$14.99
ISBN 978-0-9846480-9-2
51499>

9 780984 648092

**WOMEN of COLOR**
DAILY DEVOTIONAL

Summer
EDITION

$10.99
ISBN 978-0-9881958-2-0
51099>

9 780988 195820

# GOALS

Become an US Urban Spirit! Publishing and Media Company
Independent or Church Distributor Today!

- earn extra money
- engage with more people
- change lives
- join a winning team
- distribute high-quality
  Bibles and books

# Go to www.urbanspirit.biz

Order your Independent or Church Distributor
"Starter Kit" today online. It contains everything you need
to get started selling right away.
Or call **800.560.1690** to get started today!